ELVES AND HIDDEN PEOPLE

TWELVE ICELANDIC FOLKTALES

Almenna bókafélagið

2017

Elves and Hidden People
First published 2016 by Almenna bókafélagið
an imprint of BF-útgáfa ehf. Reykjavik, Iceland.
Selected, edited and translated by Professor
Hannes H. Gissurarson. The 1864 English
translation by George E. J. Powell and Eirikur
Magnusson of some of Jon Arnason's folktales
was often consulted, especially for the verses.

Printed in Latvia.
ISBN 978-9935-469-83-0

Contents

INTRODUCTION

For centuries, the Icelanders have during their long and dark winters sought diversion in tales about their strange compatriots, including elves and the hidden people, the two terms essentially meaning the same except that possibly elves were regarded as somewhat peculiar whereas an aura of charming mystery was attached to the hidden people.

Perhaps the storytellers felt the need in the barren and sparsely populated country to increase the number of inhabitants. It also came naturally to the Icelanders to conceive of nature as very much alive, as an enemy as well as a provider, not only offering green fields and pastures, but also active volcanoes, hot springs, snow avalanches, cold spells, drift ice and rough seas. Some of the tales undoubtedly reflect the dreams of the poor about a land of plenty, or fantasies in a prudish and puritanical age on dancing, drinking and merriment; others served to warn children not to venture too far out from the farmsteads in valleys with deep lakes and fast-flowing streams, surrounded by high mountains and steep cliffs, and all posing danger; again some are morality tales emphasising virtues like helpfulness, integrity and honesty.

The most famous collector of Icelandic folktales was librarian Jon Arnason (1819–1888), encouraged and assisted by German scholar Konrad von Maurer (1823–1902), and all but the last one of the tales in this volume are taken from Arnason's huge collection, first published in Icelandic in 1862–1864, with a selection coming out in English in 1864.

ONE

THE ORIGIN OF THE HIDDEN PEOPLE

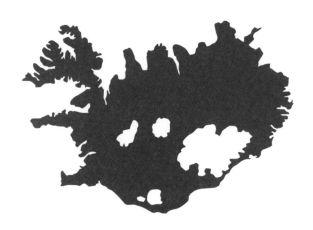

Location unknown

Once upon a time, God Almighty summoned Eve, the mother of men, and told her that at a certain time and place she should show Him all her children, freshly combed and washed and well dressed.

Eve did what she was told, but as she had many children she did not make the effort to comb and wash and dress them all up properly. She therefore chose those whom she regarded as the least presentable, hid them in a cave and closed the opening so that they could not escape. All the others she presented to God at the prearranged time and place.

When God looked at her children, He asked Eve whether she had more children, and she said no.

Then God spoke to her: "What you have now tried to hide before your God, that shall from now on be hidden to you and your husband and all your descendants except by special exception, and you shall derive no joy or benefit from them."

Two

THE FISHERMAN AT GOTUR

Location Myrdalur

Once upon a time a peasant lived at Gotur in Myrdal in the south of Iceland. During the fishing season, he often went out to sea on a rowboat to fishing grounds close to the island of Dyrholar.

One time, after landing and returning home, he had to cross a morass. In the dusk he passed a man whose horse had sunk into the bog and was stuck there. While the farmer did not know the man he helped him pull the horse up from the peat. Then the stranger said: "I am your neighbour because I live in Hvammsgil and I was just returning from the sea like you. But I am poor and therefore I cannot reward you as you deserve, but I can be of benefit to you in one way: You should never leave for the sea unless you have first seen me pass by your cottage, and then unfailingly you will be able to catch some fish." The peasant thanked him for this advice.

In the following three years the peasant at Gotur never left for sea unless he had seen his neighbour pass by the cottage, and then he never failed to make it to the sea and catch some fish. But one day the weather seemed so favourable in the morning that everybody in the neighbourhood hurried out to sea. Waiting to see his neighbour pass by, the peasant hesitated for a long time. Finally, he could not resist leaving. But when he arrived at the shore, all the rowboats were already launched and far away. However, the weather suddenly changed for the worse, and the boats were all wrecked, everybody on them drowning.

The following night the peasant's neighbour paid him a call in a dream and said: "Today, I was able to hinder you going out to sea and drown. But because you left without seeing me pass by, you need not look out for me any more. Since you did not follow my advice, I am not going to be around for you." The peasant never saw his neighbour again.

Three

THE GRATEFUL
ELF-WOMAN

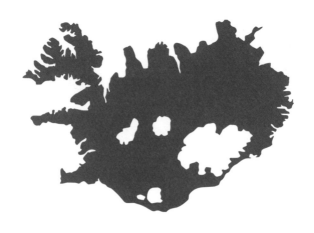

Location unknown

Once, a woman had a dream where a lady appeared, seemingly an elf-woman. This lady begged the woman to give her milk for her child, two quarts a day for a month, and to leave it in a particular place in her cottage. In the dream, the woman promised to do so. When she woke up, she remembered her promise, and for a month she put a bowl of milk every day in the designated place in the cottage, alway finding it empty when she returned. When the month had passed, in a dream the same lady paid the woman a call. She said that the woman had done well. Now she should keep the belt which she would find in her bed when she would wake up. The lady then disappeared, and the woman woke up. She then found a silver belt in her bed just as the elf-woman had said.

FOUR

THORD OF
THRASTASTAD

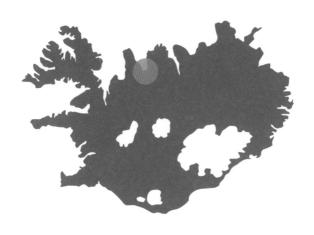

Location Skagafjordur

There was a farmer named Thord from Thrastastad in Skagafjord. He was regarded as somewhat eccentric. One day in the winter he started from home intending to go to the nearest trading village at Hofsos. There was so much snow drifting that it was easy to get lost. Thord carried a bag with his goods and took a short cut through a bog not far away from the village.

He had only walked a short distance when he lost his track. Nevertheless he went on till nightfall. Then he suddenly came across a strangely large warehouse which was lit up. He walked toward it and saw people inside, listening to music and dancing.

He went to the door and knocked. A man in a jacket opened and asked him what he wanted. Thord explained that he had lost his way and that he needed a night's shelter if possible. The man answered that certainly it was possible, "and bring in your bag. Tomorrow, I will trade with you and I will definitely not give you a worse deal than you would get at Hofsos."

Thord could hardly believe what was happening. He thought that he might be dreaming. Even if he was rather poorly dressed, the man in the jacket brought him into the main room where he met a lot of people, a woman, and some children and servants. The people were all well-dressed and singing and enjoying themselves.

Thord could hear that the man in the jacket whispered to his wife: "Here is a traveller who lost his way and is very tired. Treat him well."

She said that she felt sorry for him, stood up and fetched for him food, both good and plentiful. The master of the house came with a bottle and two glasses, pouring one drink for himself and another for Thord who thought that this was the best wine he had ever had. Everybody was merry, and Thord was far from being bored even if he found the whole situation strange. He drank glass after glass and became somewhat tipsy. Then he got a good bed and fell into a deep sleep.

The next morning Thord was given food and wine which tasted even better than that of the night before. Then the master of the house invited him to the trading room, which was full of merchandise. Thord showed the merchant his goods, receiving much more money for them than he usually got at Hofsos.

Thord now filled his bag with corn and linen and other things, at a much lower price than he was used to elsewhere. When the trading was finished, the merchant presented him with a cloak for his wife and cakes for his children. He said that Thord should benefit from having saved the life of his son. Thord wondered what he meant. The merchant said:

"Once you were standing with some other young people at a rock called Thord's Cape. You were waiting for a good wind to take you out to the island

of Drangey. Then some of the guys started throwing stones at Thord's Cape. It was a sunny and hot day, and my son was resting under the Cape: he was tired as he had been up all the night. You forbade the others to throw the stones saying that this was foolish and useless. They stopped but complained that you were really quite eccentric. If you had not interfered, they would have killed my son."

After this, Thord took leave of his host, as the sky was now clear. The merchant walked some steps with him and then wished him a safe return. Thord went his way, but when he glanced back at the warehouse, to his great surprise he saw nothing but the old Thord's Cape. Hastening home, he told his wife about the journey, showed her his merchandise and gave her the cloak.

Thord's merchandise was widely displayed and was of better quality than anything else available in Iceland or elsewhere. Thord saw the merchant never again, but all his life he kept some of this merchandise to show to people.

FIVE

GRIMSBORG: THE ELF-CASTLE

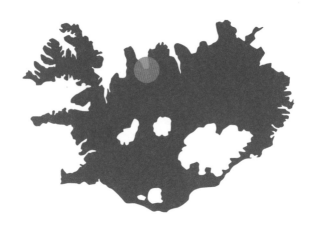

Location Skagafjordur

In the north of Iceland, near the farm Keta in Skagafjord, stands a ridge of high and steep rocks, shaped almost like a castle. It is called Grimsborg, or Grim's castle. It was said that the rocks were inhabited by the hidden people and that their leader was named Grim. There were four of the hidden people living in the rocks, two men and two women, and when mass was held at Keta two of them would usually go to church while two would stay at home.

Once the season was very bad in the north, and people were starving. One day in the spring the farmer at Keta was passing by the rocks, or the Elf-Castle. With a loud voice, he spoke in verse:

You, rich Grim of the castle, hear our sorrow!
And of your pity, before dawn tomorrow,
Cast up beneath the rocks, upon the shore,
A mighty whale, that we may starve no more.

Then he heard an answer from the castle:

Whale, come to land!
Lie stretched upon the sand
In death, that those who fear to die
From famine, find salvation nigh.

The next morning, to wit, a fine whale was found on the beach, driven there by the surf in the night. Its flesh provided food for many people and prevented a famine in the district.

Six

In the Palm of an Old Beggar

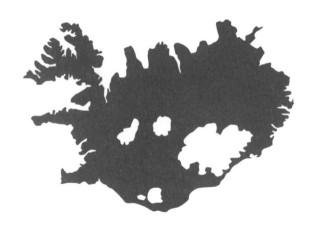

Location unknown

Once upon a time, at an Icelandic farm, the children were out playing on a grass-mound, one little girl and two somewhat older boys. When they discovered a hole in the mound, the little girl thrust her hand into it and chanted in fun:

Put something into the palm,
into the palm of an old beggar,
and the old beggar shan't see.

Then a large silver button was placed in her hand. When the other kids saw this, they became envious. The older boy thrust his hand into the hole and said the same as the girl, expecting to receive at least as much as she had. But far from it, because he only received back his own hand, having lost the use of it, never to regain it. For the elf in the mound who liked fun also hated envy, and he had given the hand a squeeze.

SEVEN

A FATHER OF
EIGHTEEN ELVES

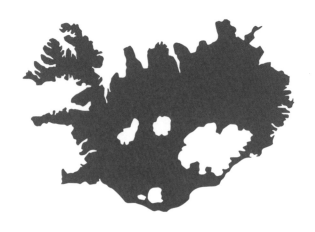

Location unknown

One summer long ago, at a farm in Iceland everybody was out making hay except the farmer's wife. She stayed at home looking after the farmhouse and her son, now in his fourth year. Already with fluency of speech, he was a precocious and promising lad. But because the mother had plenty of things to do, she had to go out of the farmhouse for a short time. She walked down to a stream close by where she washed the milk pails, leaving the kid playing in the doors of the house. Returning after a while, she spoke to the child: But now it whined and wailed loudly, surprising her greatly because previously it had always been calm, sweet and obedient. Now the only things she heard were screams and angry cries.

As time went by, the child did not say a comprehensible word, but kept yelling and crying. It ceased to grow and started behaving like it had lost its senses. The mother was at a loss. Deeply worried, she decided to seek the advice of a wise and insightful woman in the neighbourhood. Having told her neighbour about her predicament, she was asked in detail how and when this happened. The mother described how it all came to pass. When the wise woman had heard all, she said: "Don't you think, my dear, that this is a changeling? I have a suspicion that your child was replaced by an elf after you left him at the door." "I don't know," the mother said, "or could you tell me how I can find this out?" "This I shall do," the wise woman said. "Place the child just by itself, and let something catch its attention when it believes itself to be completely alone. Then it will speak. You should be nearby listening to what it says. If it says something strange and sinister, then you should spank it without any mercy until something happens." After this, they parted, and the mother thanked her neighbour for the good advice.

When the mother came home, she put a small pot in the middle of the kitchen hearth. Then she took a number of rods and bound them end to end so that the uppermost rod reached all the way to the kitchen chimney whereas the bottom rod was fastened to a porridge spoon standing in the pot. When she had done this, she fetched the boy and left him in the kitchen. She went out, leaving the door ajar, so she could see and hear what went on in the kitchen. After a while, the child began to walk round and round the pot, looking at it carefully and then exclaiming: "Now I am as old as my beard shows; the father of eighteen elve children; and yet I have never seen such a long spoon in such a small pot." The housewife then rushed into the kitchen with a big stick, snatched the changeling and started to spank it as forcefully as she could. The changeling yelled and screamed. When the woman had spanked the elf for a while, a strange lady entered the kitchen holding a young, comely

lad in her arms. She caressed him and said to the lady: "We certainly do things differently: I caress your baby, while you spank my husband." Having said this, she gave the boy back to the farmer's wife and took her husband by the hand, both of them immediately disappearing. The lad grew up with his mother, and fulfilled all the hope and promise of his youth.

EIGHT

THE CHURCH-BUILDER AT REYN

Location Myrdalur

Once upon a time a farmer lived at Reyn in the district of Myrdal. He was supposed to build a church there, but he had trouble getting the material and help for it. As the summer hay-making was approaching, he was becoming concerned that the church would not be built before winter.

One day the farmer was strolling around in his fields, worrying about the matter. Suddenly a man appeared and offered to build the church for him. The conditions were that the farmer had to tell him what his real name was before the church was completed, and that otherwise the farmer would hand over to the man his only son who was in his sixth year. They agreed on this.

The stranger started working. Aloof and close-mouthed, he devoted himself to building the church which rose rapidly beneath his hands. The farmer realized that the church would be completed before the hay-making was over. Deeply distressed, he could not find a way out of his predicament.

In the autumn when the church was near completion the farmer was wandering around outside his fields, deeply worried. He threw himself down on a grass-mound. Then suddenly he heard someone inside the mound singing, like a mother lulling a child, these words:

Soon your father Finn at Reyn will be here,
bringing your little playmate from over there.

This was repeated over and over again. Cheering up, the farmer went straight to the church. The builder had just whittled the last plank over the altar and was about to nail it down.

The farmer said: "Soon you are finishing, my dear Finn." The builder was so startled that he dropped the plank and disappeared and was never seen again.

NINE

KATLAS DREAM

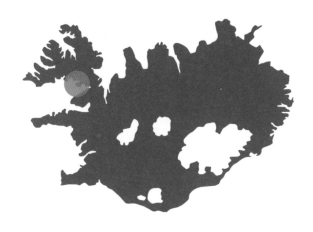

Location Reykholar

There was a prominent farmer called Mar, living at Reykholar in the Western Fjords of Iceland. His wife Katla came from good family. One summer, Mar went away to attend the Parliamentary Assembly, as was his custom, while Katla stayed at home.

One morning during her husband's absence, Katla went to bed and fell immediately asleep. At noon, her maids wanted to wake her up, but in vain. Thinking that she had died, they called her old fosterfather. When he went to see her, he realized that she was not dead as she was still breathing. He tried to wake her up, but also in vain. For the following four days and nights, he kept watch over her. On the fifth day, Katla finally woke up and seemed overcome with sorrow, while nobody dared ask her what was the reason.

Soon thereafter, Mar returned home. Now Katla was different from what she used to be because she neither came out to greet him nor did she acknowledge him when he entered the house. He asked her maids what was the reason. They said that they had no idea, but that Katla had slept unceasingly for four days and nights and not told anyone what had happened. Mar took his wife apart and asked her what had really befallen her during her long sleep, assuring her that she could ease her sorrow by sharing it with him. Katla then told him the whole story.

"When I had fallen asleep I suddenly saw," she said, "a woman enter my bedroom. She was dignified in appearance and well-spoken. She told me that she lived close by at the farm Thvera and asked me to walk with her some of the way towards it. When I agreed, she left her gloves on the bed and told me that they would be there in my place. We walked out and came to a lake where a nicely designed boat was moored. She thanked me for accompanying her, and I wished her a good trip.

She told me that her name was Alvor and held out her hand. When I stretched out my hand in return, she grasped it tightly, pushed me into the boat and rowed with me out to a small island in the lake. I felt that everything was controlled by her and nothing by me.

She spoke however kindly to me and told me that she had been compelled to do this, "and I shall later," she said, "bring you home."

We then arrived at her house in the island. It was the most magnificent mansion that I have ever seen. She took me to a room where some women were sitting. There a bath had been prepared and a bed made. I was given some delicious wine and then I fell asleep.

When I woke up, I saw a cloak lying by my side, embroidered in pure gold, and then the mistress of the house entered with other kinds of clothes, also embroidered in gold. I put all this on, and then she gave me her overcoat which was wrought with gold and lined with fur. She told me that I could keep these treasures if I wanted. She also gave me five gold rings, a golden band for my hair and a belt made of precious material.

She asked me to follow her to the great hall of the house, and it was obvious that she was in command. We were eight women in all going there. The hall was lavishly decorated; gold-embroidered tapestry hang from the walls; silver boxes and gold-plaited drinking horns were on the tables. Many people were present there. Besides the high table I saw a bed where a man dressed in rich silk was lying asleep. Alvor went to him, woke him og called him Kari.

He asked why she had disturbed him and whether she had some news to tell, "Or has Katla arrived?"

Then he saw that I was indeed there. Kari and I were then led together to the high table where we sat down and Alvor asked people to call him the bridegroom. People did so and spent the day drinking and celebrating. At nightfall, Alvor said that I should go to bed with Kari. I replied that nothing could be further from my mind and that I loved Mar so much that I would never take pleasure from being with another man. Alvor replied that it would have serious consequences for me if I would not allow Kari to have his way.

I was at a loss because I now felt like a lamb in a pack of wolves. When I went to bed, Kari came to me and offered my all his gold and other treasures, but I refused to make love to him. He then asked me to drink from a horn from which he had himself drunk previously and told me that he would rather die than to see me in sorrow. He comforted me and promised me that he would have me brought home soon.

I dwelt there for two nights, in sorrow. Everybody tried however to please me. Then Kari told me that we would be expecting a son together. He wanted me to call him Kari. He gave me a splendid belt and a fine knife and told me to pass it on to our son, because they were family heirlooms. He told me to put all my dresses and other treasures into a sack and take them with me.

"You should show all of this to your husband, Mar," he said, "and tell him the truth about it, even if you may feel embarrassed by it. The two of you should move to the Thvera farm. There, you will find two small hillocks where my house stood and they will be full of money. You will have many illustrious descendants. Now I have to leave you and I shall never meet you again: I don't know how long I shall live after this."

Then Alvor took my hand and led me out of the house. I heard a loud sound when Kari collapsed in sorrow over me and died.

Alvor rowed with me on the boat across the lake and brought me home and took her gloves out of my bed.

As she left, she said to me: "May you do well, Katla, even if you have only caused me grief by breaking the heart of my son. Enjoy your treasures."

"Thus finished my dream," Katla said, "and I expect you, Mar, as an honourable man to feel sympathy for me and to forgive me, as I did none of this out of my own free will."

Mar asked her to show him the treasures, and so she did.

In the spring of the following year Katla gave birth to a handsome boy. He was called Kari, as his father had requested, and Mar behaved to him as if he was his own son. He doted upon him unlike his mother who did not much care for him. The couple moved to Thvera, in accordance with what Katla had said, living there happily ever after.

TEN

HILD, QUEEN
OF ELVES

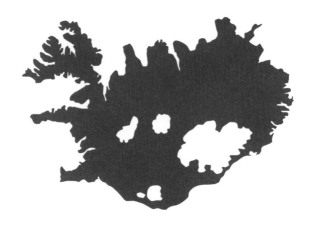

Location unknown

Once upon a time there was a farmer living in a mountainous region of Iceland. He was unmarried, but his housekeeper's name was Hild, of whose family he knew nothing. She was in charge of everything indoors, handling her tasks well. She was pleasant to everyone, including the farmer. But they were not intimate, as she was a quiet woman and reserved, even if always polite.

Everything was going well for the farmer except that he had difficulty in finding shepherds, whom he badly needed for his many sheep. The difficulty was neither that the farmer was mean nor that the housekeeper was ungenerous with food and other necessities. The reason was rather that the shepherds did not last long: they were usually found dead in bed on Christmas Day.

In those days the custom was to go to a Midnight Mass on Christmas Eve and it was regarded as no less important to attend church then than on Christmas Day. But on the mountain farms it was not easy for a shepherd, looking after his flock, to go to church in time.

The shepherd did not however have to guard the farmhouse on Christmas Eve, as was considered necessary. Hild invariably took care of this, also making all the necessary preparations for the festivities, such as cooking and cleaning, usually staying up late into the night so that those who attended church had returned and gone to bed and were fast asleep, before she herself went to bed.

When one after another of the farmer's shepherds were found dead on Christmas Eve, word got around and the farmer found it increasingly difficult to hire a shepherd for his farm. He was himself under no suspicion of having brought about the deaths of the shepherds as they all seemed to have died naturally. Finally, the farmer decided that irrespective of what would happen to his farm, his conscience did not allow him to hire more shepherds who would almost certainly die.

Soon after the farmer had made this final decision and was therefore not hiring any shepherd, a man, appearing bold and strongly built, visited him, offering his services.

The farmer said: "I do not need your services and I shall not hire you."

The stranger said: "Have you hired a shepherd for next winter?"

The farmer said no and told the stranger that he had no intention of doing so, "And you must know of the extraordinary things which have happened to my shepherds."

"I have heard of this," the stranger said, "but their fate doesn't frighten me if you are ready to hire me."

The stranger kept on urging the farmer to hire him, and finally the farmer gave in. As time went by, the two of them got on well with each other, and the other people at the farm also liked the shepherd because he was well-behaved, fearless and forceful in all kinds of circumstances.

On Christmas Eve the farmer kept the custom of going to church with all his people, leaving behind only the housekeeper and the shepherd with his flock.

In late evening the shepherd came home as usual, eating and going to bed. It occurred to him however that it might be prudent to stay awake rather than to go to sleep and to see what would happen even if he felt no fear or foreboding.

Late at night he heard the farm people return from the church. They had a late bite and then they all went to bed. For a while, nothing happened, and the shepherd found himself becoming very sleepy, being tired from his hard work during the day. But he mustered all his energy to stay awake.

Then he heard someone creeping up to his bed. Recognising the housekeeper, Hild, he pretended to be fast asleep while she put something into his mouth. While he realized that this was a magic bridle, he did not resist.

When Hild had bridled him, she led him out, mounted him and rode hard on him until she came to a place which appeared to him to be a deep pit or cleft in the earth. She dismounted behind a rock, fastened the reins to it and leapt into the pit.

The shepherd felt uncomfortable being tied to the stone. He was also curious to know what was happening to Hild who, now, seemed to him to be a very strange and mysterious person. What he did was to rub his head against the stone until the bridle fell out of his mouth and he was free.

Then he leapt into the pit into which Hild had disappeared. He had not gone far when he saw Hild in front of him. She was walking rapidly through a smooth and lush grassland.

The shepherd realized that if he would follow Hild across the grassland she would immediately see him, and then something might happen to him. He therefore took a stone of invisibility that he used to carry with him and put it into his left palm. Then he started running after her as fast as he could.

When he went further into the field, he saw that Hild was heading towards a great and splendid palace. He also saw that a crowd of people came out of the palace in order to welcome her. Foremost amongst them was a very distinguished-looking man who seemed to greet her as a wife. The others seemed to salute her as their queen. The leader of the group was accompanied by two adolescents who embraced Hild with great warmth, as if she was their mother.

When all these people had welcomed the queen, they followed her and the king to the palace where she was received with the appropriate pomp and ceremony. She was dressed in royal robes and rings of gold were put on her fingers.

The shepherd followed the crowd to the palace, taking care not to be in the midst of the throng, but being able nevertheless to watch the spectacle. Inside the palace, he saw more adornments that he had ever been able to imagine. Food was put on a lavishly decorated table. After a while he saw Hild enter the great hall of the palace, dressed in her royal robes. She sat down at the high table besides the king, while the courtiers took their places on both sides of the table. In a while, a sumptuous feast began.

Afterwards, the table was removed and some of the men and women of the court started dancing with one another. Others watched the spectacle, while the king and the queen had a private conversation, in a tender and sad manner, the shepherd observed.

While the king and queen were deep in conversation, three children, younger than those already mentioned, ran into the hall and welcomed their mother. Queen Hild responded lovingly. She picked up the youngest one and put it on her knee and caressed it. But the child was restless and noisy, and the queen put it back on the floor, took a ring from her finger and gave it to the child. For a while, the child played with the ring but then lost it on the floor.

Standing close by, the shepherd was quick to seize the ring when it fell on the floor. He put it in his pocket without anyone noticing. Everybody thought it however strange that the ring could nowhere be found.

When the night was far advanced, Queen Hild made preparations to leave. But all the people in the palace begged her to stay longer and became very downcast when she refused.

The shepherd had noticed an old and grim woman sitting in a corner in the palace. She was the only one there who had neither welcomed Queen Hild nor was urging her to stay longer.

When the king saw that Hild was insisting on leaving, despite the appeals of himself and of others, he went up to this old woman and said: "Please withdraw your curse, mother, as I have begged you to do, so that my queen does not have to live far away and be of such little joy to me as has now been the case for a while."

The old woman answered angrily: "My curse is still in full force, and there is no chance at all that I shall withdraw it."

A silence fell upon the king, and he went grief-stricken to his queen, put his arms around her and kissed her and continued tenderly to beg her to stay. The queen said that she could not do so because of his mother's curse. She added that she regarded it as likely that they would not be able to see each other ever again because of the curse. The reason for the many deaths that had taken place could hardly be kept secret any more and she would eventually have to answer for them, even if she had brought them about unwillingly.

While Hild was speaking, the shepherd went quietly out of the palace, across the field to the pit and up it. He put the stone of invisibility in his pocket, and the magic bridle in his mouth and waited for Hild.

In a short while, Hild arrived, alone and dejected. She mounted the shepherd and rode on him home to the farm. When they arrived, she put the shepherd carefully into his bed and removed the bridle, went herself to bed and was soon asleep.

While the shepherd was wide awake during all this, he pretended to be sleeping for Hild not to notice anything. But when she had gone to bed, he went into a deep sleep and slept long into the next day, as was to be expected.

On the morning of Christmas Day the farmer was the first one to rise, fully expecting to witness the same misfortune as in years past: a shepherd dead in his bed. As the other people also woke up, he walked to the bed of the shepherd and touched him with his hand. He then sensed that the shepherd was alive. Greatly relieved, the farmer thanked God profusively for his mercy.

Then the shepherd woke up and dressed, appearing fit and healthy. The farmer asked him whether anything had happened during the night.

The shepherd said no, "But I had a strange dream."

The shepherd then told the people present the whole story of the night, starting by Hild coming to his bed and bridling him and then every detail that he could remember.

When he had finished the story, everybody fell silent except Hild. She said: "What you are saying can be dismissed as totally untrue, unless you can present some evidence for it."

Sure of himself, the shepherd presented the ring that he had picked up during the night from the floor of the elf palace and said: "Even if I do not really have to present evidence for a story about a dream, it so happens that here I have proof that I was spending the night with elves, or is this not your gold ring, Queen Hild?"

Now Hild said: "Indeed it is, and you are the luckiest and most blessed of men because you have released me from the curse laid on me by my mother-in-law and which had forced me against my will to perpetrate a lot of misdeeds." She then told her story:

"I am an elf-woman coming from a humble family. But the present king of the elves fell in love with me. Against the will of his mother, he married me. Furious, his mother told her son that he would only be able to see me occasionally, and each time it would cost a man's death. The curse she laid on me was that I would be a common maid in the upper world and that I would have to kill a man every Christmas Eve in such a way that I would bridle him when he was asleep and ride on him as I rode on the shepherd last night, to meet the king, and then ride so hard on

him back that his heart would break and he would die. Finally, my misdeeds would be discovered and I would be condemned to death, unless I could find such a gallant and spirited man that he would dare to follow me down to Elfland and would also be able to prove it afterwards.

While the previous shepherds of the farmer here all died as a result of my actions, I hope that I will not be punished for this, because it was all against my will. This true champion here has been the first to explore Elfland and to release me from the curse, and I shall reward him in due time.

I am not going to dwell here any longer, and thank you very much for all your help, but now I want to return home." Then Queen Hild vanished from sight, and has never been seen again.

The shepherd married and in the next spring built his own farm, with some support from his former employer. Becoming a prominent farmer in the district, his counsel and support was often sought by his neighbours. But his popularity and good luck were so abundant that they seemed to be created by two persons rather then one. He himself ascribed his prosperity to Hild, Queen of Elves.

ELEVEN

CROSSWAYS

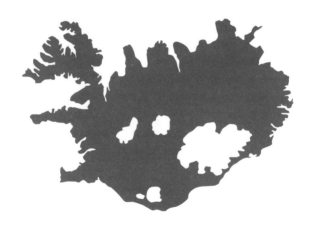

Location unknown

It is said that crossways are to be found on mountains or hills where there is a view to four churches. When people sit at such a crossway on Christmas Eve, then elves come from every direction and ask them to go with them, but one must ignore them. They offer all kinds of treasures, gold and silver, fine dresses, wonderful food and drink, but, again, one must not accept anything. Elf-women also arrive in the shape of one's mother and sisters and beg one to come, using all kinds of tricks.

But at dawn one should stand up and say: "The Lord be praised, now daylight fills the heaven." Then the elves disappear, leaving the treasures behind to be kept by the people present. But if one replies to the elves or accepts their offer, then one becomes bewitched and goes mad, never to regain one's senses.

On the night of one Christmas Eve, a man called Fusi dwelt outside at a crossway. He long resisted the various blandishments of the elves, until finally a elf-woman came with mutton-suet and offered him. Then Fusi looked up and said what has since become a common saying in Iceland: "Rarely have I refused a bite of mutton-suet." He took a bite and became mad.

Twelve

Fair Was the Land

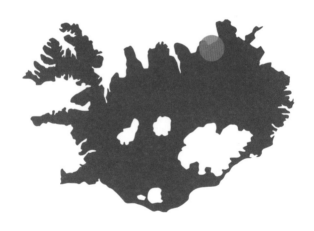

Location Kelduhverfi

On the farm Sultir in the district of Kelduhverfi, in Northeastern Iceland, there was once a young cowherd who had the daily task of driving the cows from there towards the next farm, Vikingavatn, where they grazed on some pastures.

Besides the trail between the two farmsteads lies a ridge of rocks which almost looks like a man-made wall. According to legend, some hidden people were living in these rocks. A large and lush bush of redwood grew out of one of the rocks. Each time the cowherd passed by it, he used to break a small branch off the bush, to use as a whip on the cows.

As summer passed, the boy continued this practice and the bush declined until it totally vanished. In the coming autumn, some strange illness was visited on the boy. First he lost the use of his hand, and then of most of his body, and eventually he withered away and died.

Somewhat later, an old shepherd from Vikingavatn named Odd happened one day to be near these rocks. He then heard a voice coming from inside them, humming ruefully:

Fair was the land which my father once had.
Therefore I'm crying and feeling so sad.

It is said that the bush destroyed by the boy had been a place of celebrations for the hidden people.

Now they had punished the cowherd by bringing about his illness and death.